I love my Daddy

Colour the Story

Illustrated by Brenna Vaughan and ~~~~~~~~ tatty (You!)

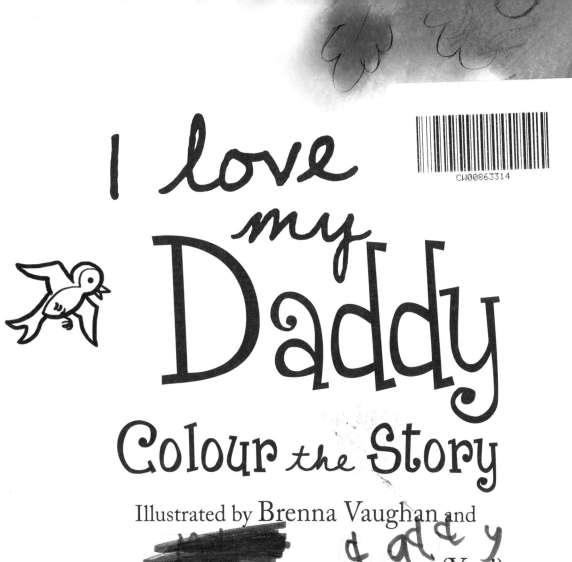

This edition published by Parragon Books Ltd in 2014

Parragon Books Ltd
Chartist House
15–17 Trim Street
Bath BA1 1HA, UK
www.parragon.com

Please retain this information for future reference.

Written by David Bedford   Illustrated by Brenna Vaughan and Henry St Leger
Edited by Lily Holland   Designed by Kathryn Davies
Production by Richard Wheeler

ISBN 978-1-4723-3642-2

Printed in China

I love my Daddy

Colour the Story

Illustrated by
Brenna Vaughan

Written by
David Bedford

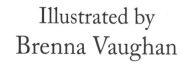

PaRragon

Bath • New York • Singapore • Hong Kong • Cologne • Delhi
Melbourne • Amsterdam • Johannesburg • Shenzhen

This is Little Squirrel and his daddy.
They love playing together in the woods.

Who else is playing in the trees?
A rabbit family? Or you and your daddy?
Draw them in and colour the picture.

One day, Little Squirrel went out to play with his daddy. Little Squirrel wanted to show Daddy Squirrel all the things he could do.

"What shall we play first?" said Daddy.

"I know," said Little Squirrel excitedly…

Colour the animal
families and draw some
more animal friends
in the woods.

"Digging! Look, Daddy!" said Little Squirrel, as he dug, and dug, and dug, with his little tail wagging.

Colour in Little Squirrel and Daddy Squirrel.

"Well done!" said Daddy.

But suddenly, Little Squirrel's tail stopped wagging.

"Help, Daddy!" cried Little Squirrel. "I'm stuck!"

Who else lives inside this hole?
Draw in an animal who lives underground.

Daddy Squirrel helped Little Squirrel wriggle out
of the hole, and gave him a soothing hug.

"You are a good digger!" said Daddy. "What shall
we play next?"

*Use your stickers to
decorate the grass.*

"Climbing! Look, Daddy!" said Little Squirrel, and he climbed as high as he could go, looking around as far as he could see.

"Well done!" said Daddy. But suddenly Little Squirrel closed his eyes tightly...

*What do you think is high in the sky with
Little Squirrel? Butterflies? Or birds?
Draw them in then colour in the picture.*

"Help, Daddy!" cried Little Squirrel.
"I'm stuck!"

Daddy Squirrel helped Little Squirrel climb down and gave him a soothing hug.

"You are a good climber!" said Daddy. "What shall we play next?"

Colour the picture.

"I know… jumping! Look, Daddy!" said Little Squirrel, and he jumped, and jumped, and jumped with a big smile on his little squirrel face.

*Draw a grassy hill for Little Squirrel to jump
on and decorate it with your stickers.*

But suddenly Little Squirrel stopped smiling, and…

Splat!

"Help, Daddy!" cried Little Squirrel. "I'm stuck again!"

Daddy Squirrel helped Little Squirrel out of the sticky mud and gave him a soothing hug.

"You are good at jumping!" said Daddy.
But Little Squirrel shook his head sadly.

*Colour in Little Squirrel
and his daddy.
Draw some pretty butterflies
in the sky.*

"I don't want to play any more,"
said Little Squirrel. "I always
get stuck. I can't do anything!"

Daddy Squirrel lifted Little Squirrel
high on to his shoulders.

"Let's play together," he said.

Colour in the picture.

"Let's run!" cried Daddy Squirrel.
Little Squirrel held on tightly as
they whooshed through the woods.

"Yippeee!" he shouted.

Can you spot the birds,
butterflies and rabbits
playing in the trees?
Colour each one in as
you find it!

"Let's climb!" said Daddy Squirrel. Little Squirrel kept his eyes open wide as they reached the top of a tree.

"Wheeee!" he shouted.

Finish colouring the tree that Daddy Squirrel and Little Squirrel are climbing.

What other animals are climbing the tree? Draw them on this branch.

"And now," said Daddy Squirrel, "let's jump!"

Little Squirrel and Daddy Squirrel jumped…
and jumped… and jumped!

But suddenly…

What other animals are good at jumping?
Draw them jumping with Little Squirrel.

Splat!

"Oh help!" cried Daddy Squirrel. "Now I'm stuck!"

Little Squirrel giggled as he helped his daddy out of the sticky mud.

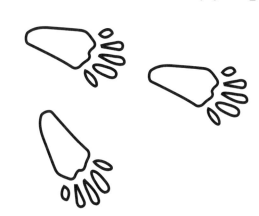

Fill this page with Daddy Squirrel's muddy footprints.

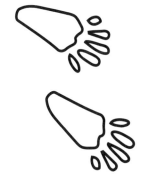

"You can do everything, Little Squirrel!" said
Daddy Squirrel proudly, as they washed their
muddy paws in the stream. "You can even save
a Daddy Squirrel!"

Little Squirrel climbed high on to his daddy's
shoulders again.

"I love playing with you, Daddy," he said.
"And… I love my daddy!" shouted
Little Squirrel as they raced
home happily together.

Colour Daddy Squirrel,
Little Squirrel and all of their
friends as they play together.

That night, Little Squirrel curled up to sleep
with Daddy, and dreamed of his adventure.

Colour in Little Squirrel's dream.